My Shopping

by Anne Giulieri

photography by Sylvia Kreinberg

This is a banana.
It goes here.

Special

BANANA
Perfect snack with smooth creamy taste
Product of Australia

£1.38 bag

49

£1.74

£3.49

£2.62

£1.64

£2.0

value

value

value

value

value

3

This is a pear.

It goes here.

This is a carrot.
It goes here.

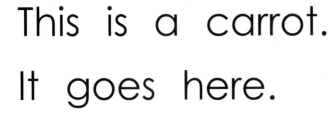

This is a tomato.
It goes here.

This is a sausage.

It goes here.

This is a cookie.

It goes here.

This is a cake.

It goes here.

RB ROLLS £2.30

RC CAKE MIX CHOCOLATE £3.49 SAVE

Here is my shopping.